Magnificent Mazes

Anna Nilsen

How to Play
Find out through the time tunnel.

TIME TUNNEL

3

Sometimes you will have to go backwards as well as forwards.

4

Jump through time tunnels.
DO NOT CROSS THEM.

6

You can go across landing pads.

8

The ending place will be labelled like this.

Homer ends here

7

You will know you have reached the correct time zone when you see your chosen character and their destination spot here at the bottom of the page.

Homer ends here

5

When you jump through a time tunnel you will arrive on a landing pad. Chose a path and carry on.

10

Chose another character or go to the back of the book for more fun.

Homer Starts here

2

Lead your chosen person through the maze...

1

Homer

Chose someone from a tab and find them in the picture.

LANDING PAD

How to Play

Follow the numbers 1 to 10 and learn how to play the game.

9

Each person has lost three things along the way. They will appear here. Can you find them on their route?

Homer

at the Olympic Games, Greece 500 BC.

On his travels back to his own time zone,
Homer lost these three things. Can you find them?

Abraham Lincoln starts here

 Cleopatra
on the banks of The Nile, Egypt 48 BC.

 Cleopatra ends here

This is squishy!

Cleopatra ends here

On her travels back to her own time zone,
Cleopatra lost these three things. Can you find them?

 Eric the Red
at his settlement in Newfoundland, 986.

On his travels back to his own time zone, Eric the Red lost these three things. Can you find them?

Yum, yum!

Cleopatra starts here

We've caught you

William the Conqueror
at the Battle of Hastings, England 1066.

William I ends here

On his travels back to his own time zone, William the Conqueror lost these three things. Can you find them?

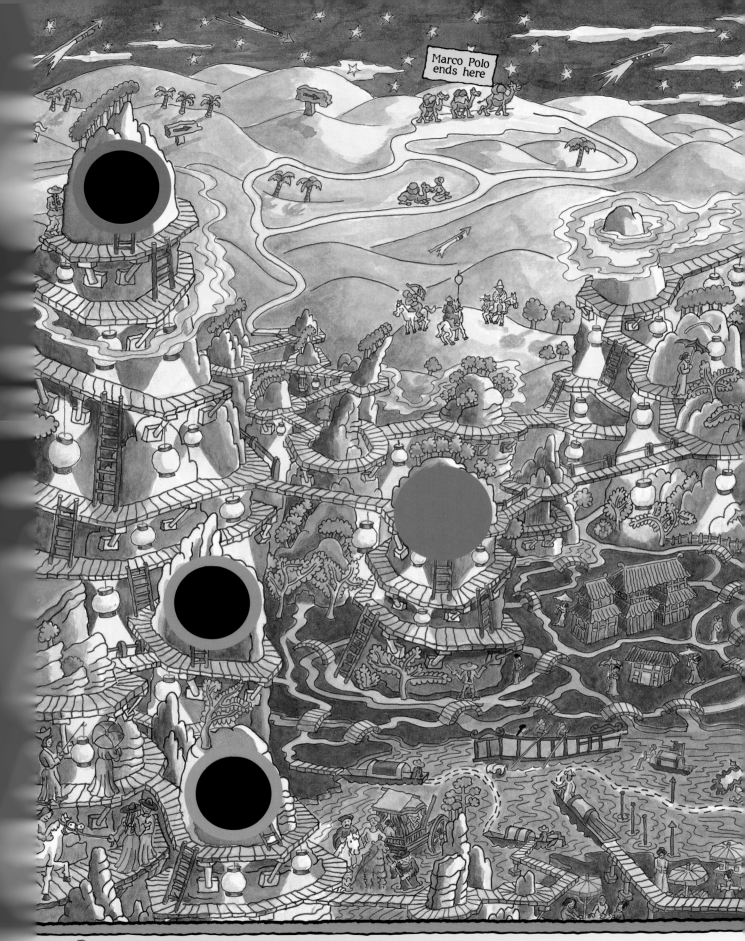

Marco Polo

in the Gobi Desert, China 1272.

Marco Polo ends here

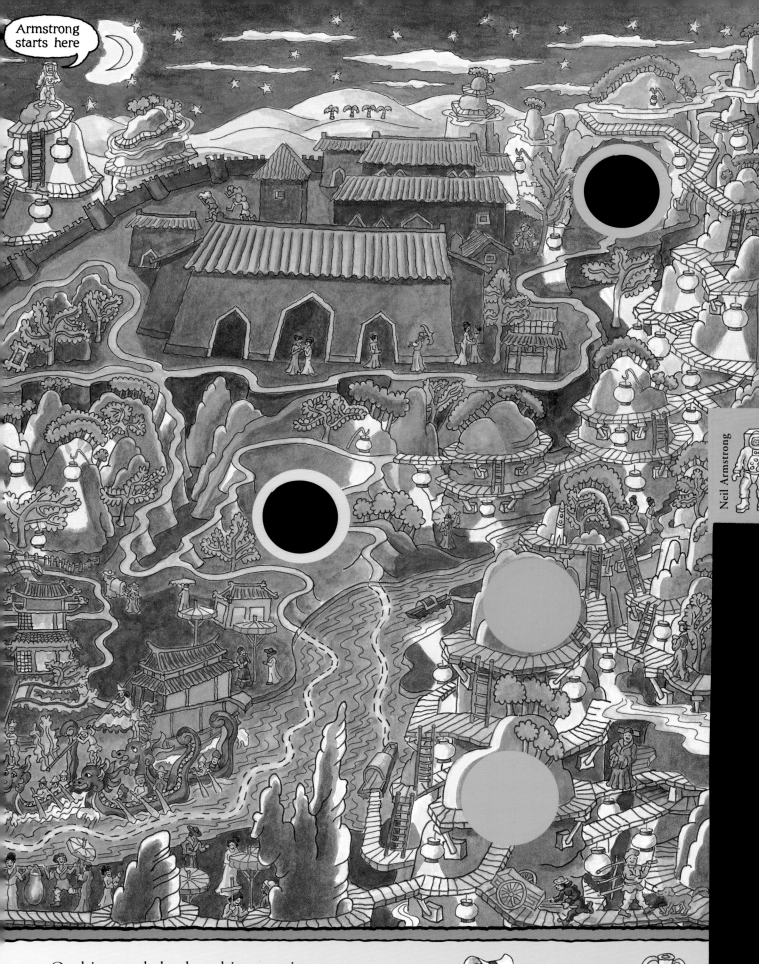

Armstrong starts here

Neil Armstrong

On his travels back to his own time zone,
Marco Polo lost these three things. Can you find them?

 Leonardo da Vinci
in Florence, Italy 1502.

 Leonardo ends here

On his travels back to his own time zone, Leonardo da Vinci lost these three things. Can you find them?

 William Shakespeare
at The Globe Theatre, London, England 1599.

On his travels back to his own time zone, William Shakespeare lost these three things. Can you find them?

 Mozart

in the Belvedere Gardens, Vienna, Austria 1780.

On his travels back to his own time zone, Mozart lost these three things. Can you find them?

Abraham Lincoln
in the Wild West of America, 1850.

On his travels back to his own time zone, Abraham Lincoln lost these three things. Can you find them?

William I

Neil Armstrong

walks on the moon, 1969.

On his travels back to his own time zone, Neil Armstrong lost these three things. Can you find them?

Shakespeare

Europe

Asia

Africa

Australia

Indian Ocean

Homer
Greece 500 BC

Cleopatra
Egypt 50 BC

0

Eric the Viking
Newfoundland
800

William the
Conquerer
Hastings 1066

Marco Polo
China 1200

North
America

Atlantic
Ocean

South
America

Pacific Ocean

**William
Shakespeare
London 1588**

**Abraham Lincoln
USA 1850**

**Neil Armstrong
USA 1969**

2000

Leonardo da Vinci
Florence 1500

**Mozart
Vienna 1775**

Telescope Game

How much did you really
see on the maze routes?
Look at these views
and work out where they
came from.

Vikings fighting the
local people, called
'Skraelings'.

Mozart's pet starling
which inspired some
of his music.

The Chinese Kublai
Khan hunting with
his pet cheetah.

Sir Edmund Hillary,
the first man to climb
Everest in 1953.

Friends beating
an athlete with sticks
to help him win.

Lion-hunting in the
desert – a pastime
of the Pharoahs.

Barbed wire, which
was invented in 1874
to help fence in cattle.

Petty criminals, left in
the stocks having old
food thrown at them.

Grapes picked in
Newfoundland which
was known as 'Vinland'.

Michaelangelo's colossal
statue of David carved
out of marble.

Shields made to stab
in the ground and
form a wall.

Hippos which were
often hunted to stop
damage to farmlands.

A giraffe, given to the
Medici family zoo by
the Egyptian Sultan.

Alcock and Brown
making the first non-stop
Transatlantic flight in 1919.

Sign posts put out at night by Marco Polo while on his travels.

A boxing ring formed by four men holding out sticks.

Khon the Wanderer - God of the Moon and help to the sick.

Harold, killed in battle so that William could be crowned king.

The chuck-wagon – a mobile kitchen for cowboys on the trail.

Guy Fawkes, burnt for trying to blow up the Houses of Parliament in 1605.

Savanarola, ruler of Florence, hanged and burned for heresy.

This man who is using an early form of hearing aid.

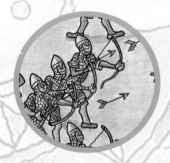

These invading French soldiers had the advantage of bows and arrows.

Buffalo – North American Indians depended on them for their livelihood.

Some of New York's famous skyscrapers, including the Empire State Building.

Decapitated heads, left on stakes to deter others from crime.

This lady who is selling poetry as we would sell magazines.

Statues of cheats, put together to form the Avenue of Cheats.

Arrows of fire made with gunpowder invented in China.

A camp – 'Viking' comes from an old word meaning a camp.

The Olympic Games, Greece 500BC

Successful athletes at the Olympic games were celebrated in victory poems composed by famous poets like Homer. Unfortunately little is known about the greatest poet of Ancient Greece, whose works were told and not written down until long after his death.

Homer

Log book

Who they were and when they lived.

The River Nile, Egypt 48BC

The beautiful and powerful queen of Egypt, Cleopatra, presented herself to the Roman general Julius Caesar, rolled up in a rug. She then recruited Caesar to help her get the throne back from her brother and she continued to reign until her death.

Cleopatra
69BC-30BC

Newfoundland 986

Eric the Red was outlawed from his country of Iceland and became a famous Viking rover and founder of the first Scandanavian settlement. His son Leif Eriksson, was the first person to land in America at Newfoundland.

Eric the Red
950-1005

Hastings, England 1066

William the Conqueror lived in Normandy but claimed to be the real King of England. His army attacked and beat English troops in a famously bloody battle at Hastings on 14th October 1066, which was recorded on the Bayeaux Tapestry.

William I
1027-1087

The Gobi Desert, China 1272

When he was seventeen the Venetian traveller and writer Marco Polo went to China with his tradesman father. He spent many years serving in the court of the Mongol ruler the Kublai Khan and wrote a fascinating account of his stay.

Marco Polo
1254-1324